MW01096876
To Avery,
Loved meeting you!
Julie Chapman
xoxo

WITCHES, BATS, AND MYSTICAL CATS

Spooktacular Rhymes for Halloween Time

by

Julie Chapman

Introduction

What is it about Halloween that makes your heart tingle? Do you love ghost stories? How about the delicious treats? Is it finding the perfect costume? There is just something special about Halloween that encourages you to wonder, dream, and create.

This book contains poetic stories about this bewitching season and the adventures that await us. Some tell chilling tales of haunted houses, old cemeteries, and mysterious legends. Others detail the fun side that celebrates the beauty of fall, the make-believe, and the colorful candies.

As if under a witch's spell, Halloween can inspire you to be your most imaginative. Always hold on to that enthusiasm that allows you to believe in *what could be.*

Published in 2021 by
Saratoga Springs Publishing, LLC
Saratoga Springs, N.Y. 12866
www.SaratogaSpringsPublishing.com
Printed in the United States of America

ISBN-13: 978-1-7353735-8-4
ISBN-10: 1-7353735-8-3
Library of Congress Control Number: 2021901000

Written by Julie Chapman
Illustrations by Anthony Richichi
Graphic Design by Patrick Jankowski
Publisher & Book design by Vicki Addesso Dodd

This book is dedicated to
Mark, Luke, and Amanda.
The magic in my life.
Thank you for your constant encouragement.

And with love to
my mom and dad,
Teresa and Robert

Table of Contents

The Mystical Cat will stay with you.
Spot him as you journey through.

Who Will You Be?

The sun starts to set, fall leaves are blowing,
A chill fills the air, the harvest moon glowing.
It's Halloween night, a rare time of year,
When witches and zombies begin to appear.
The streets fill with characters, scary and sweet,
Scampering door-to-door in search of a treat.
In the small town that we call home,
There are plenty of places where goblins roam.
The houses line up, one by one,
You hit them all, as you make your run.
Before it starts, you plan your attack,
You need to prepare more than your sack.
You can't be yourself, tonight you *must* change,
Choose something cute, scary, or strange.
The question becomes, "*Who will you be?*"
Because half of the fun is what others will see.
Remember, it's more than a mask and a cape,
This night is for you to briefly escape.
Dream big and choose something special to be,
For on Halloween, *your imagination is free.*

How You Spot a Witch

The fall night sky looks mysteriously bright,
Some say there's *magic* in that moonlight.
When clouds are thin and there's a clear view,
You may be lucky to spot a witch or two.
They love to travel on Halloween night,
The question is how to catch the sight?
Pick a dry spot, put a blanket down,
Make sure it's a quiet place in town.
Stare up at the moon around midnight,
That's the best time to see witches in flight.
Look for movement in a cloud that's thick,
A flicker of light shoots from the broomstick.
Witches are dressed in pointed black hats,
They're wearing long capes, and flying with bats.
Their journey is quick, so try not to blink,
They move a lot faster than you may think.
If it's a calm night, and you listen well,
You'll hear a witch cackle and whisper a spell.
If you make this your mission, don't do it alone,
Witches are savvy, and *may follow you home.*

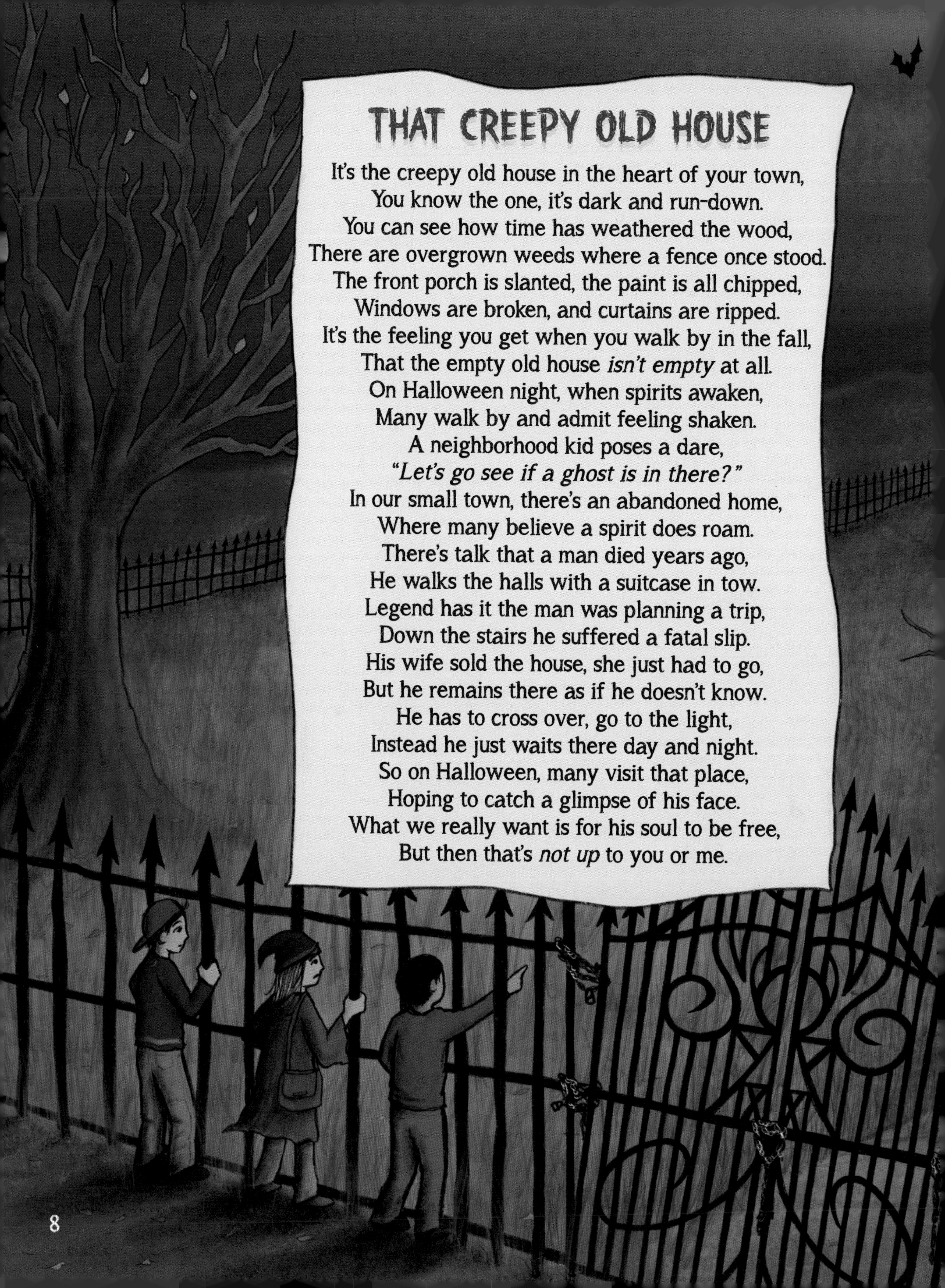

THAT CREEPY OLD HOUSE

It's the creepy old house in the heart of your town,
You know the one, it's dark and run-down.
You can see how time has weathered the wood,
There are overgrown weeds where a fence once stood.
The front porch is slanted, the paint is all chipped,
Windows are broken, and curtains are ripped.
It's the feeling you get when you walk by in the fall,
That the empty old house *isn't empty* at all.
On Halloween night, when spirits awaken,
Many walk by and admit feeling shaken.
A neighborhood kid poses a dare,
"Let's go see if a ghost is in there?"
In our small town, there's an abandoned home,
Where many believe a spirit does roam.
There's talk that a man died years ago,
He walks the halls with a suitcase in tow.
Legend has it the man was planning a trip,
Down the stairs he suffered a fatal slip.
His wife sold the house, she just had to go,
But he remains there as if he doesn't know.
He has to cross over, go to the light,
Instead he just waits there day and night.
So on Halloween, many visit that place,
Hoping to catch a glimpse of his face.
What we really want is for his soul to be free,
But then that's *not up* to you or me.

THE FEARED FELINE

Halloween stirs images of pumpkins and bats,
And there's plenty of mystery surrounding *black cats.*
They have piercing green eyes, they're shiny and sleek,
They're typically friendly and not very meek.
But some say black cats bring us bad luck,
This all goes back to a stigma that stuck.
Many feared witches lived centuries ago,
They were evil and linked to darkness below.
They would practice magic in the woods at night,
And nocturnal cats were a frequent sight.
Legends say these cats were feared the most,
Because they resembled a witch's cloak.
Also at night, they were hard to see,
So a stronger connection came to be.
If witches were evil, then black cats were too,
That's what many people believed to be true.
But we know that black cats are misunderstood,
They're beautiful creatures, so loving and good.
This Halloween give a black cat some love,
And remember that *all cats* are gifts from above.

Perfect Pumpkins

Get in the car, it's time to go,
To the farmer's field where the pumpkins grow.
Halloween is coming, the clock is ticking,
Bright orange gourds are ripe for picking.
You search to find the perfect one,
Hunting around is half of the fun.
Clean off your pumpkin, lay newspaper down,
Cut off the top, start digging around.
Pull out the guts, scoop it all clean,
Carve out a face, happy or mean.
Don't throw out the seeds, toast them with butter,
A touch of sea salt will make your heart flutter.
Put in a candle and light up the head,
This tradition is meant to scare off the dead.
Jack-o-lanterns adorn the front of your home,
Where trick-or-treaters will eventually roam.
Make sure your pumpkins are easily seen,
They're meant to *protect you* on Halloween.

Gilly's Perfect Pumpkin Seeds
- Clean pumpkin seeds well.
- Preheat oven to 400 degrees.
- Boil seeds in salted water for 10 min.
- Strain seeds and put them in a bowl.
- Toss with butter, olive oil, sea salt, and pepper.
- Spread out seeds on sheet tray
- Roast for 30 minutes.
- When golden brown, they're done.
Enjoy!

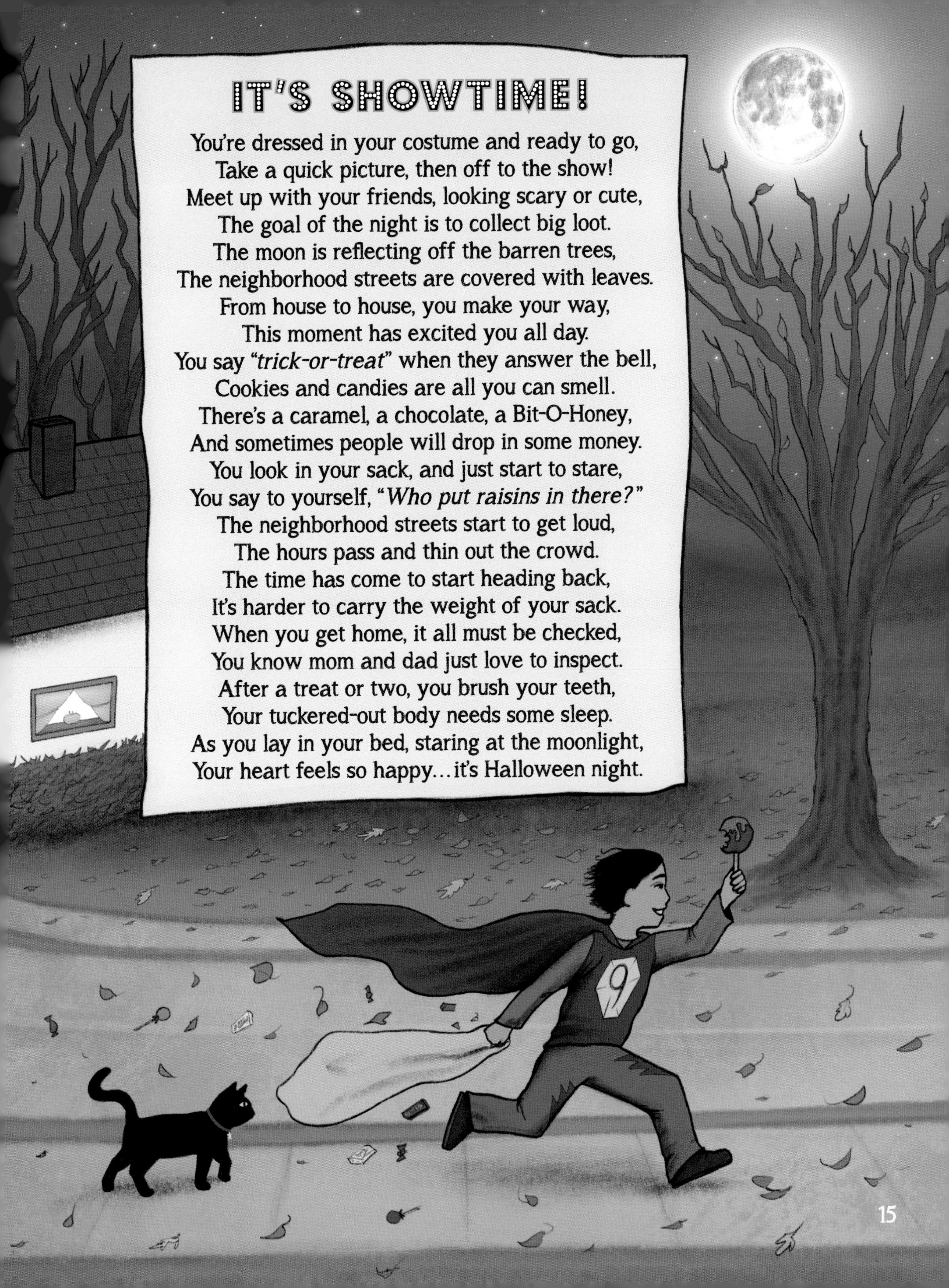

IT'S SHOWTIME!

You're dressed in your costume and ready to go,
Take a quick picture, then off to the show!
Meet up with your friends, looking scary or cute,
The goal of the night is to collect big loot.
The moon is reflecting off the barren trees,
The neighborhood streets are covered with leaves.
From house to house, you make your way,
This moment has excited you all day.
You say "*trick-or-treat*" when they answer the bell,
Cookies and candies are all you can smell.
There's a caramel, a chocolate, a Bit-O-Honey,
And sometimes people will drop in some money.
You look in your sack, and just start to stare,
You say to yourself, "*Who put raisins in there?*"
The neighborhood streets start to get loud,
The hours pass and thin out the crowd.
The time has come to start heading back,
It's harder to carry the weight of your sack.
When you get home, it all must be checked,
You know mom and dad just love to inspect.
After a treat or two, you brush your teeth,
Your tuckered-out body needs some sleep.
As you lay in your bed, staring at the moonlight,
Your heart feels so happy... it's Halloween night.

YOUR HALLOWEEN BASH

You look forward to this party every fall,
It's time to throw your Halloween ball.
Your house is covered in bright orange and black,
Long tapered candles have blood-dripping wax.
Witches are hanging from the porch light,
Zombies pop out of the ground at night.
The dangling ghosts swing from the trees,
The fog machine blows smoke at your knees.
As your Halloween guests arrive at your place,
Your morgue will spark an abrupt about-face.
Your buffet features eyeballs made of eggs,
There are chocolate spiders with licorice legs.
After experimenting with a soda or two,
You've concocted the perfect witches brew.
Throw on your costume, you've spent a ton,
But don't feel bad, it's all in good fun.
Get ready to crank up the Monster Mash,
It's almost time for your *Halloween Bash*!

HAPPY HALLOWEEN!

THAT ICONIC TREAT

Caramel apples, Sweet Tarts, chocolate Kisses,
All of these candies are so delicious.
But on Halloween there's only one,
That's a classic staple of all of the fun.

With bright colors of yellow, orange, and white,
The triangle layers are sure to delight.
The tiny cones have a marshmallow flavor,
The chewy texture helps you to savor.

In the late 1800s this unique treat was born,
Called "Chicken Feed" because it looked like bird corn.
The more people shared it, a new name came about,
"Try Candy Corn" is what people would shout.
It quickly became a popular treat,
As the world embraced this waxy sweet.
A.G. GOELITZ
CONFECTIONERY
COMPANY.
It's now a perfect symbol of everything fall,
Halloween being in the heart of it all.
So, get a big bag and be sure to stock it,
It's *good luck* to have a few in your pocket.

BEWARE

He lurks in the shadows of trick-or-treaters at night,
He makes sure to stay far away from the light.
He's tall and he's thin, he's slightly bent over,
He's dressed all in black, a cloak covers his shoulder.
He's cold and he's pale, his lips ruby red,
He has silky black hair that flows from his head.
He's eerily handsome, his smile suspicious,
He looks as if he sees something delicious.
There's an energy around him that draws you in,
A magical force that comes from within.
He's compared to a bat in legends today,
That's because they both live off the blood of their prey.
Feeding his thirst is how he's found fame,
But the person who's bitten is never the same.
If you spot this fine fellow, just continue your trek,
Chances are he's most likely a *pain in the neck*.

THE SCARECROW MYSTERY

Drive by Gilly's farm on any fall day,
There's a curious man in the thick of the hay.
He's held up by a post eight feet in height,
There are layers of rope that hold him up tight.
He wears a plaid shirt, his blue jeans are worn,
His clothing is dirty, messy, and torn.
He has on work boots and gloves made of leather,
His tattered straw hat has been beaten by weather.
His arms stretched way out, secured to their beams,
Wads of hay stuffing are bursting his seams.
This is no ordinary scarecrow you see,
On Halloween night ... *there's a mystery.*
His pole has been spotted bent to the ground,
And our beloved friend is nowhere to be found.
You can see his footprints in the moonlight's glow,
Where he travels to, no one seems to know.
Legend has it he visits a loved one he's lost,
Who comes alive on this night in the midst of the frost.
Some believe that this scarecrow does have a soul,
By the rooster's call, he's back on his pole.
So this Halloween night, if you can stay awake,
You may be the *first person* to catch his escape.

The Most Powerful Spell

Is there something you want? What do you need?
Is there a desperate desire you hunger to feed?
Are you looking for love? How about more money?
Do you dream of a place that's warm and sunny?
Anything you wish is possible, they say,
You just need to believe, work hard, and pray.
But to ensure you're doing all that you can,
Here's an *incantation* to add to your plan.

This is a spell you can easily do,
To help your heart's desire come true.

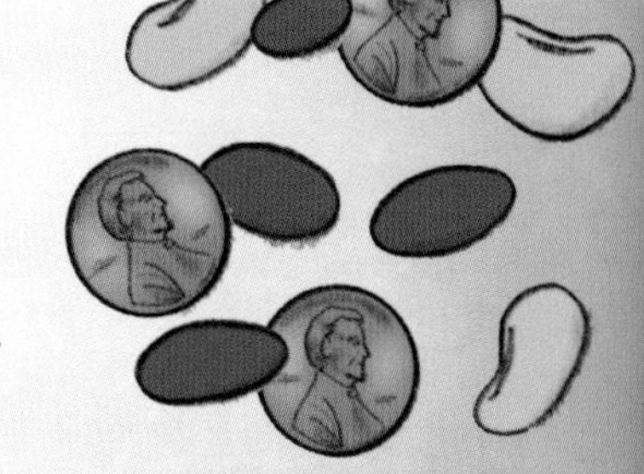

Grab three pennies,

And a handful of beans,

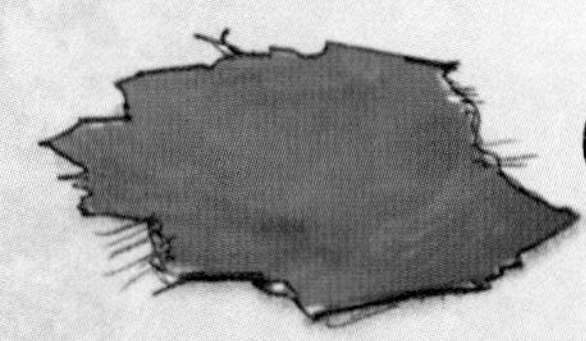

Rip off some cloth from old blue jeans.

Write down your wish on a piece of wood,
It has to be something that brings only good.

Find a grassy spot close to a creek,
Then dig a hole about eight inches deep.

Whisper this phrase as you bury it all,
"I ask Mother Earth to hear my call."

In a short time, your wish will come true,
But there's something else you need to do.

Be generous, kind, and learn to forgive,
There's power in how you choose to live.
Be grateful for the gifts in your life today,
Because that's how more will come your way.

Counting Fall Blessings
School is back in session and it's getting colder,
A sweater is needed to cover your shoulder.
October brings beauty to the northeast,
A colorful landscape, to say the least.
The mountains are bursting with orange and maroon,
The water at night reflects the bright moon.
When you step outside, you smell the air,
The scent of fall sweeps through your hair.
It's that time of year for football tackles,
Soccer games and picking apples.
Your heart flutters as you hop on a bike,
Take a long stroll, or go for a hike.
Occasional storms usher in the rains,
They bring down the leaves and clog up the drains.
The days are getting shorter as the winds roll in,
The season's true beauty is about to begin.
When the harvest is done, the farmers will rest,
It's this time of year when we truly feel blessed.

10

HAUNTING HOWLS
Every month when the moon is perfectly round,
Its lunar glow reflects off the ground.
There's a strange power in that shiny sphere,
Some say it's a sign that *danger* is near.
On a full moon night, go sit under its beams,
From the still of the woods you'll hear frightening screams.
The howling comes from mysterious creatures,
Who have both human and wolf-like features.
They hide in the brush and try not to be seen,
These blood-thirsty monsters are hungry and mean.
They've lost control, they want to kill,
It's a desperate desire they need to fill.
Legend has it they're cursed or under a spell,
When the sun comes up, all seems to be well.
So on Halloween night, if there's a full moon,
Don't let your fear cause you to swoon.
If a werewolf finds you, put up a fight,
There's an infectious venom if he takes a bite.
And if you do survive becoming his feast,
The next full moon, then *you'll be the beast.*

Souls Adrift

Everyone knows on any given night,
It's creepy to visit a local gravesite.
On the outskirts of town, there's an old cemetery,
It's been so neglected, it looks pretty scary.
The headstones are tilted, the names are all worn,
The grass is overgrown, and the flags are all torn.
The wood fence is broken from fallen trees,
The walkways are covered with sticks and leaves.
The place feels abandoned with no one in sight,
But some say *that changes* on Halloween night.
Curious folks walk the hallowed ground,
They claim to have seen several spirits around.
They say that they float with an eerie glow,
And appear to have lived centuries ago.
They seem so sad as they glide through the pines,
It looks as if they feel left behind.
So this Halloween, as the wind sweeps the leaves,
Honor those souls as they drift through the trees.

FRIGHT NIGHT

It's finally October, colder nights have arrived,
The moon appears brighter, it's darker outside.
This time of year tickles your heart,
A *magical season* is about to start.
To get into the spirit of Halloween,
Play a scary movie on your TV screen.
Make buttered popcorn, call your friends over,
It's much more fun sitting shoulder-to-shoulder.
Hocus Pocus, Casper, or Ichabod Crane,
That Headless Horseman will drive you insane.
Horror movies can make your heart race,
You watch for a moment, then cover your face.
Some good advice as you hunker down,
Avoid the films with a creepy clown.
When the night is over and your friends leave,
You admit feeling shaken by the make-believe.
But don't worry about what's consuming your head,
I'm sure it's a *nice monster* under your bed.

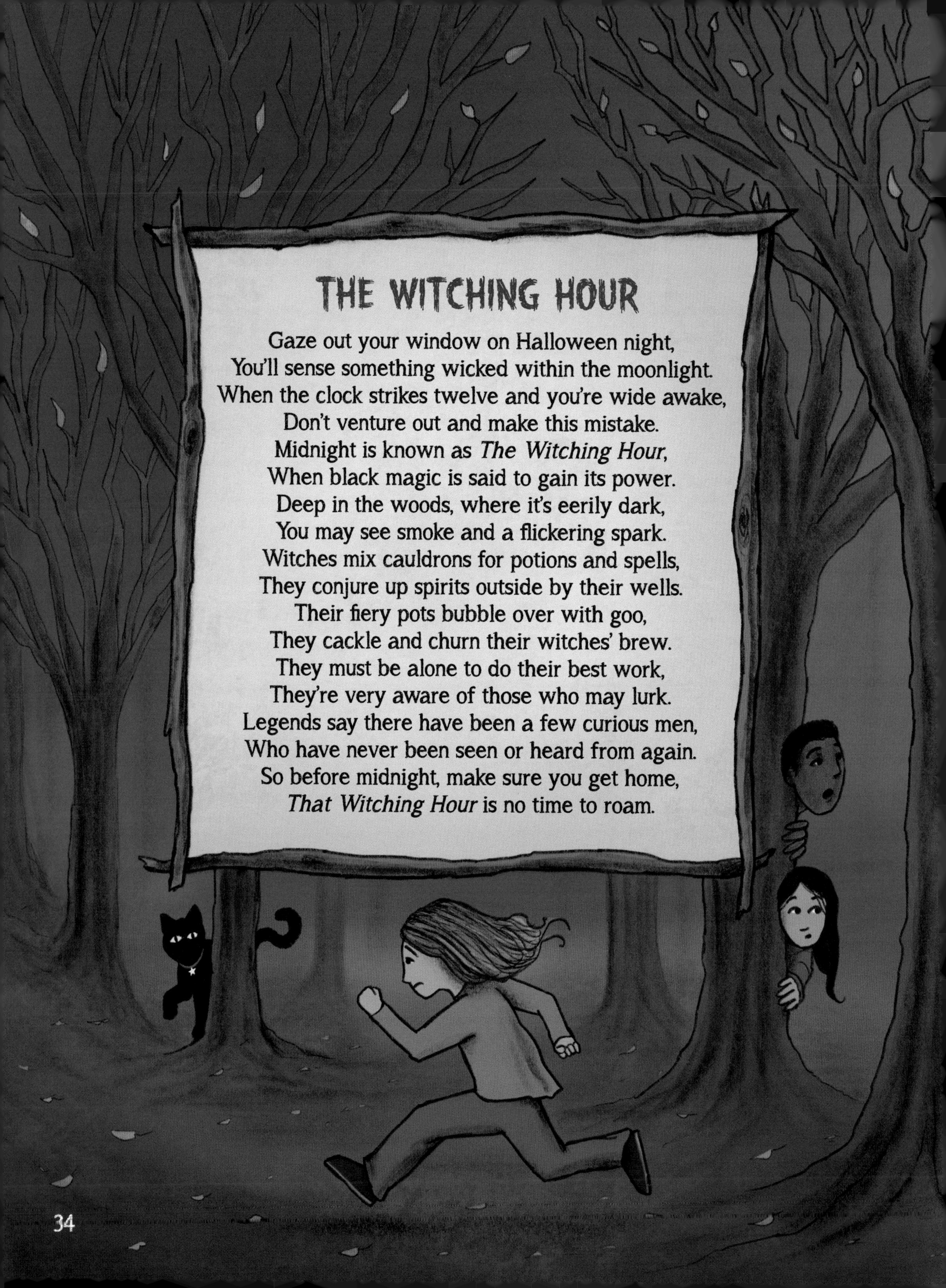
THE WITCHING HOUR
Gaze out your window on Halloween night,
You'll sense something wicked within the moonlight.
When the clock strikes twelve and you're wide awake,
Don't venture out and make this mistake.
Midnight is known as *The Witching Hour*,
When black magic is said to gain its power.
Deep in the woods, where it's eerily dark,
You may see smoke and a flickering spark.
Witches mix cauldrons for potions and spells,
They conjure up spirits outside by their wells.
Their fiery pots bubble over with goo,
They cackle and churn their witches' brew.
They must be alone to do their best work,
They're very aware of those who may lurk.
Legends say there have been a few curious men,
Who have never been seen or heard from again.
So before midnight, make sure you get home,
That Witching Hour is no time to roam.

We love Halloween stories of ghosts and witches,
There are thrilling pictures of zombies with stitches.
It's the one night of the year when many attest,
That spirits can awaken from eternal rest.
To honor the legends, we enjoy traditions,
We throw in some candy and fun superstitions.
Halloween can be a magical time in your life,
To escape a world full of chaos and strife.
This is when your imagination is free to soar,
To come alive and create like never before.
As we witness society change with the seasons,
There are limits placed on us for various reasons.
Fear is a powerful force in the world today,
It can often discourage your excitement to play.
The challenge for you is to never let go,
Of that youthful spirit that helps you to grow.
You're happiest when you're free to imagine,
Trying new things, or pursuing a passion.
Like the harvest moon, your heart shines a light,
Your job is to keep it strong and bright.
If your inner jack-o-lantern ever starts to dim,
Just embrace and encourage *that child within.*

WITCH way to the party?

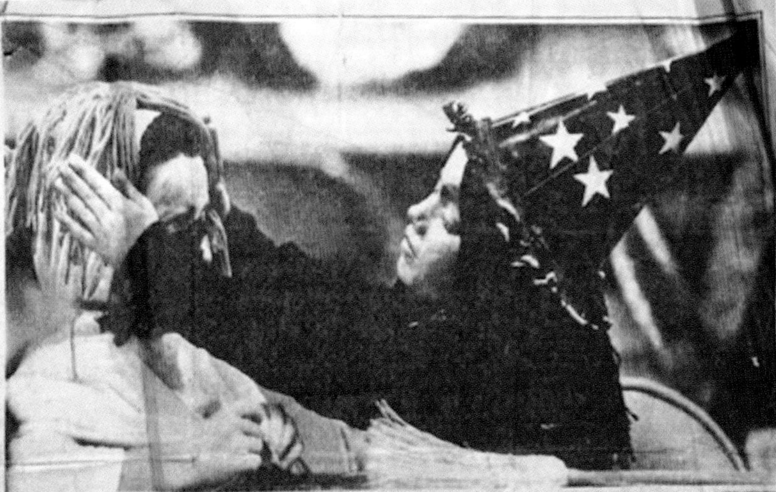

Beware the witching hour

...'cause screaming demons march through the streets

By ANDY SMITH

"If you ever scream in my ear like that again, I'll kill you," said one mother as she stood on the steps of the YMCA in Johnson City.

But who wouldn't scream after being chased by the werewolf, scared by the Phantom of the Opera and grabbed by Frankenstein as the wind howls and weird cries echo through the cloudy night?

As Halloween approaches, monsters lurk behind every bush, under every tree.

They are currently lurking in the Johnson City YMCA, for example, courtesy of the Johnson City Jaycees and Jaycees, who are presenting a haunted house through October 31st.

Steve Sarnowski of the Jaycees said he expected about 1,300 persons to go through the haunted house last night. Cost of a tour through the house is $1.25 for families or 50 cents a person.

"I just like to do it," Penn said through his mask.

Several hundred other costumed characters also marched down Clinton Street in the annual Halloween parade sponsored by the Clinton Street Merchants Association and the Binghamton West Kiwanis Club.

The parade also featured country and polka bands, drum and bugle corps, antique cars, fire trucks, floats and even a smiling, waving politician — city councilman Stephen Yevchak.

Even the windows on the street wore Halloween costumes — they had been painted by neighborhood school children with witches, monsters and pumpkins.

Clinton Street was lined with spectators — many of whom were costumes themselves — cheering on the marchers and catching candy thrown from the floats.

Some witches use bats eye's and turtle teeth, but Julie Chapman, 8, of 47 Thompson St., Binghamton, uses a little patience to arrange [illegible] for the Catholic Youth Organization Halloween party yesterday at St. Mary's Church, 37 Fayette St., Binghamton.

ME

1978

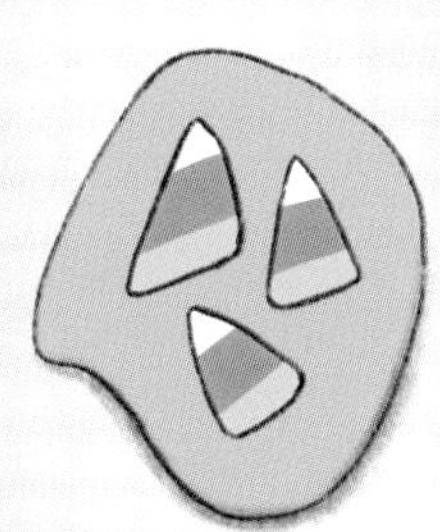

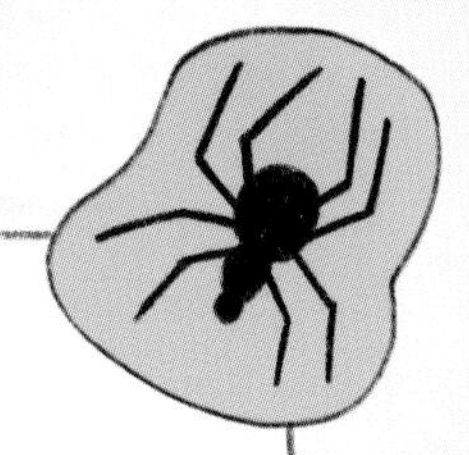

My Inspiration for this book is . . . YOU

When I was 8 years old, I was super excited about transforming into an old green witch. After all, it was Halloween and I needed to look scary. My mom and I found a black lace vintage dress at a local thrift shop. I went home, put it on, painted my face green, and threw on a cardboard witch hat with silver glittery stars. I then made my way to our community Halloween party where I not only looked like a witch, I pretended to be one the entire time. I cackled, I snarled, and I cast countless spells. I ended up winning first prize for best character and I even had my picture printed in the local newspaper.

I don't remember what I won that day, but I vividly remember how I felt. My heart was bursting. Halloween encouraged me to become someone or something else with endless magical possibilities. I let my imagination take me on a joyful journey. For the first time in my young life, I felt free. *What a feeling*!

Since that day, I have always loved Halloween and how it can fuel our ability to visualize and create. But as I started to witness society diminishing this important holiday, I became even more passionate about encouraging others to embrace its magic. By combining my love of poetry with the thrills of the season, I created this book for *you*.

Love,

Julie